SCIENCE.......

for the academically talented student

e a

and the National
Science Teachers
Association

SCIENCE

*for the Academically Talented Student
in the Secondary School*

Report of a Conference sponsored jointly by the National
Education Association Project on
the Academically Talented Student and the National Science
Teachers Association.

Chairman:

ROBERT R. DONALDSON

Professor of Science
State University Teachers College
Plattsburgh, New York

National Education Association
Project on the Academically
Talented Student and National
Association of Science Teachers,
a Department of the National
Education Association.

1201 Sixteenth Street, N.W.
Washington 6, D. C.

375.5
N2TTs

FOREWORD

EDUCATION serving a democracy demands a climate for learning in which challenge is consistent with capacity. Respect for differences among individuals is the hallmark of such an education. Opportunity consistent with ability cannot be the same for all students. This is particularly significant for the academically talented student, who has not always enjoyed the benefits of special consideration. "Opportunity to go as far as he can" means opportunity for the rapid learner as well as for all the others.

To this end, this publication has been prepared with the aid of a grant from the Carnegie Corporation of New York. A group of educators competent in the area of science and selected from both secondary and higher education, in cooperation with the National Science Teachers Association, met in conference for three days under the chairmanship of Robert R. Donaldson, Professor of Science, State University Teachers College, Plattsburgh, New York. This report is a summary of the discussion and suggestions resulting from the conference for developing a program for the academically talented in science at the secondary-school level.

In a sense, this publication is a sequel to the Report of the 1958 Invitational Conference on the Academically Talented Secondary School Pupil. It says, insofar as the members of the conference can say this, that certain areas should be taught at each grade level of the secondary-school; that we ought to bring a good deal of what is generally taught in the tenth and eleventh grades into the junior high-school grades eight and nine; and that this material should be taught in depth. In other words, this publication says that most bright students can learn many concepts earlier and that they can explore these with considerable discernment.

These suggestions must, of course, be considered in the context of each school in which they might be implemented. It is clearly understood that recommendations meeting the needs of the academically talented student must differ significantly from school to school. It also seems certain that the most appropriate and practical administrative procedures which provide for identification, ability grouping, and even counseling are of little value unless content, methods, and appropriate subject sequence are adapted to the specific needs of the academically talented pupil.

There is a demand for excellence in the education of each, up to the level of his capacity—a demand which is the measure of the health of our society. Perhaps, by the implementation of this philosophy and these suggestions, we can give a still more significant meaning to learning experiences within each discipline and thus to the school life of all youth.

I particularly want to express my appreciation to Margaret J. McKibben, Assistant Executive Secretary of the National Science Teachers Association, for her most valuable work in the preparation of this publication.

CHARLES E. BISH, *Director*
Project on the Academically
Talented Student

4

CONTENTS

AN INTRODUCTORY STATEMENT

THE NATIONAL Science Teachers Association has long been concerned with the education in science of academically talented high-school students. The Science Achievement Awards program, sponsored by the American Society for Metals and conducted by the Future Scientists of America Foundation of the National Science Teachers Association, is now in its eighth year. A student publication, *Tomorrow's Scientists,* is in its third year. Other booklet-type publications have been produced for these students.

For some time the FSAF had been planning a service booklet for teachers who work with these capable students in science. When plans were developed for expanding the National Education Association's report on the academically talented in the various subject-matter areas, it became evident that this project and that of FSAF involved certain common interests and objectives. Thus it seemed advisable to work together.

Plans for a joint NEA-NSTA conference on the education of the academically talented high-school science student were begun. The conference was held last December. The present report which developed from it has been made possible through funds provided by the Future Scientists of America Foundation of NSTA and a grant from the Carnegie Corporation of New York to the National Education Association's Project on the Academically Talented Student.

It is hoped that this report will be of help to teachers and school administrators throughout the country.

HERBERT A. SMITH, *President*
ROBERT H. CARLETON, *Executive Secretary*
National Science Teachers Association

Identification of the Academically Talented Science Student

ROBERT R. DONALDSON

AT NO time in the past has such interest been shown in the basic discoveries of science and engineering. Scientific knowledge has ballooned to such proportions that it has become a major influence in the economic, political, and cultural patterns of civilized man. The marvels of electronic communication and atomic energy had hardly been appreciated by the general public before the overwhelming reality of artificial satellites and space rockets was upon us. Concurrently, medical science has made great strides in developing antibiotic cures for disease, in producing innoculation serums for body protection such as those developed for preventing polio, and many other life-saving methods. Yet, impressive as these discoveries have been, their true worth is secondary to the creative genius and inventiveness of the human mind which made their development possible.

The importance of recent scientific successes is unquestioned, but of even deeper significance is the continuing endeavor of that dedicated, versatile, creative, professionally minded group we know as "scientists," for, in reality, it is the perpetuating vision of the human mind that has made possible these fundamental advances in understanding and invention. As a result, one of the commanding issues faced by mankind in the mid-twentieth century is the resolution of the intellectual climate which best engenders a growing and challenging desire on the part of able-minded and imaginative youth to push back the horizons of science still further.

Lest we become overly possessed with progress in scientific research per se, we must recognize the inter-relationship of science with the other liberal studies and the importance of integrated intellectual efforts in meeting the demands of a complex society. It must be acknowledged that creative minds are as necessary to the humanities, the fine arts, and the social studies as to the sciences. The spirit of equitability in utilizing talent is perhaps best expressed by Henry A. Moe:[1]

> The intelligence of the citizenry is a national resource which transcends in importance all other resources. To be effective, that intelligence must be trained. The evidence shows that many young citizens of high intelligence fail to get the training of which they are capable. . . . Plans for the discovery and development of scientific talent must be related to the other needs of society for high ability. Since there never is enough ability at high levels to satisfy all the needs of our complex civilization for such ability, we would not seek to draw into science any more of it than science's proportionate share.

It is clearly the responsibility of our educational institutions to provide the optimum conditions under which the intellectually capable will be challenged to make their creative contributions. What positive plans of action might be considered by the typical high-school in working with able students during their formative years? It was for this purpose that approximately 200 educators and interested laymen assembled at Washington, D. C., in February of 1958 to combine their efforts in making general suggestions for teaching the academically talented that would apply to all disciplines at the secondary-school level. The purpose of this pamphlet is to extend the "guidelines" concerning science in

---

[1] Moe, Henry A. "Report of the Committee on the Discovery and Development of Scientific Talent." *Science the Endless Frontier, A Report to the President.* (Edited by Vannevar Bush.) Washington, D. C.: Superintendent of Documents, Government Printing Office, 1945. Appendix 4.

8

the report [2] of that conference and to provide specific examples which illustrate basic educational principles that are pertinent in working with students talented in science. The deliberations of a committee of science-educators (listed on p. 57-60) were guided by the major topic headings established during the February 1958 conference and constitute the content of this report. It would be presumptuous even to imply that the suggestions found in this report are meant to be all-inclusive. Rather, it is hoped that the reader will critically evaluate what has been proposed as points of departure for further individual consideration and extension.

Anyone familiar with the traditions of American education realizes that no fixed philosophy, course of study, administrative procedure, or teaching technique can be mandated for all schools to follow. Nor would this be desirable. Instead, local autonomy is expected to prevail in establishing policies of suitable grade placement of subject matter, a satisfactory marking system, a balanced curriculum of required and elective courses that meets the needs of the community, and a class schedule that is conducive to the teaching-learning process. Such decisions must necessarily be tempered by local conditions and be consonant with sound educational practice. It is understood that local school administrations screen from educational research findings and practices at other schools those suggestions that seem to offer the greatest promise in the local setting. It is with this in mind that the considered views expressed in this report should be weighed and evaluated before actual incorporation into an administrative plan of action.

Certain organized practices for working with talented youth have been publicized in recent years and should

---

[2] Invitational Conference on the Academically Talented Secondary School Pupil. *The Identification and Education of the Academically Talented Student in the American Secondary School.* Washington, D. C.: National Education Association, 1958. p. 109-116.

receive administrative consideration. For some schools "ability grouping by subject" has proven very successful, but this would be difficult to establish in a small rural high-school. Contrariwise, some smaller high-schools have been able to promote "acceleration" of their better students through close student-teacher working relationships that would not be possible in large high-schools. So, whether acceleration, ability grouping, enrichment in regular class, advanced placement, downgrading of subjects, or other practicable plans for working with the academically talented are to be adopted, it should be the decision of the local school administration.

At this conference it was generally accepted that the term "academically talented" refers to a student with an intelligence quotient of 120 or more. The group thus included would comprise the top 15-20 per cent of the high-school students in the United States, and it is to this level of ability that the various suggestions in this pamphlet are directed. However, it should not be assumed that a high score on an intelligence-type test qualifies a student as being talented in *science*. Other factors may be as important in this determination as general intelligence, though always supported by it. These qualities usually conform to a broad configuration of abilities and interests that vary considerably from student to student.

Since able science students are characterized by a multiple pattern of abilities, it is only reasonable that many evaluating devices should be used in attempting to identify them:

- First and foremost, there should be in each local school system an efficient system of record files extending from kindergarten through twelfth grade. These should include anecdotal records as well as objective test scores.
- Trained guidance personnel should be available for student consultation and alert to the problem of

10

identifying the science-talented. There should be a close working relationship between counselors and the science-teaching staff.

- A continuing program of testing should be maintained both for measuring general intelligence and special aptitudes. Except for the "late-bloomers," high academic ability can be identified quite reliably by the seventh or eighth grade. Regression is noticeably low between the grades of seven and twelve.

- Multiple factors should be considered in identifying able science students. These should include general intelligence and other standardized test scores, past class records, teacher evaluation, expressions of student interest in science, individual characteristics, and special abilities.

- The process of identification should be flexible enough to utilize new measures of individual competence in selection and continuous in operation so that individual students may enter special programs for the talented without penalty. Similarly, students who find the particular program too rigorous should be allowed to resign from it without prejudice.

It is obvious that all of the evidence cannot be objectively measured. Hence, the judgments of guidance personnel and science teachers should serve as guideposts in improving the process of selection for any program developed for the talented in science.

Content in Science for the Academically Talented Student

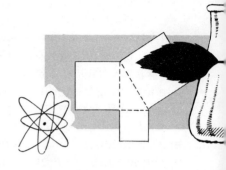

RUTH E. CORNELL, Chairman,
ALEXANDER TAFFEL, Recorder

GROUP PARTICIPANTS: Brown, A.; Hess, W.; Jacobson, W.;
Laster, H.; Metzner, J.; Paulson, R.; Slesnick, I.; Tompkins, E.;
Van Hooft, G.; Williams, H.

WE LIVE on the threshold of a new era in exploration, an era introduced by that dramatic adventure in worldwide collaboration of many individuals and organizations in many countries which we call the International Geophysical Year; an era when a new adventuresome spirit is emerging in the world as man crosses the threshold of space and as cultures and nations everywhere are in flux—a state of mind, let us note, strikingly like that which pervaded European culture after Columbus' discoveries, when new lands beckoned, new knowledge was ever more freely and effectively sought, tremendous new ideas appeared which led to, among other things, the establishment of nations founded, like our own, upon principles of freedom and democracy. But our age is also an era marked by political turmoil unmatched in human history. An expanding search for sounder knowledge and the strongest possible efforts to use the best we know as fully as we can have become imperative. Human survival itself now requires the search and the efforts; and it is certain that, without these, a society which realizes the best, not the worst, in man is impossible.

Mindful of these circumstances, the committee made two recommendations regarding the teaching of academically talented students in science.

1. In addition to a rich program of science in grades seven, eight, and nine and a comprehensive program of science in the elementary grades, each talented student in *science* should have a minimum of a three-year sequence equivalent to the present basic courses in biology, chemistry, and physics and a minimum of three years of mathematics in grades nine through twelve. In addition, elective courses should be available to enable these students to pursue further special interests in particular science areas. In certain cases, mathematics, as an elective in the twelfth year, might be more desirable if a choice between mathematics and science is necessary.

For the gifted student the Committee on Content in Science favored electives that are consistent with the guidelines suggested in this report. These electives would fall into two general groups, those that are meant to permit pursuit in depth of specific areas in one of the basic sciences and those that have this objective and are also designed to permit advanced placement in college.

It is recommended that advanced placement courses be revised on agreement between the colleges and high-schools in order (a) to provide better continuity in the total science program and (b) to emphasize broad concepts of science. In either case, a high level of achievement should be maintained.

Typical electives in various fields other than advanced placement courses might be:

    Microbiology
    Field biology
    Advanced general chemistry (utilizing techniques of qualitative and quantitative analysis)
    Atomic physics
    Electronics and electricity
    Geophysics
    Mathematics (fourth year)

History of science (or case histories)
Astronomy
Earth science
Geochemistry.

2. Special ability grouping is desirable for science-talented students where the local situation makes this possible. In schools where grouping is not feasible the responsibility still rests upon the teacher, school, and community to provide an enriched science program for the talented science student in line with the remainder of this report. Every way in which the teacher can individualize his contacts with the able student should be emphasized. Provisions should be flexible enough so that the "late-bloomers" may enter the curriculum for talented students without prejudice to themselves.

It would be presumptuous—as well as obviously impossible—for a small group in a limited time to lay out an entire sample curriculum or any complete sample courses. Clearly, too, no single way of organizing subject matter is *the* best one for all teachers, schools, or pupils. Instead, the committee has identified nine fundamental guidelines for the selection and organization of subject matter, illustrating each of them by a few arbitrarily selected examples taken from the different disciplines of junior and senior high-school science. These are intended *only* to make the principles more clearly understandable to readers of this report.

Guideline 1

The content should be developed in the light of contemporary scientific thinking and theorizing. As often as possible, pupils should glimpse the frontiers of scientific investigation. They should come to understand that neither our knowledge nor our understandings is static, that further proving by research opens up new areas of investigation and modifies current ideas.

14

a. In seventh or eighth grade a unit on the universe and the solar system is often developed. With academically talented students, the study of this unit may include a consideration of modern theories of the origin and evolution of the universe, galaxies, and the solar system. Young people should also be given an opportunity to learn about modern methods of studying the universe and solar system, such as the use of radio telescopes as well as optical telescopes; the use of tools for analyzing light waves and radiations from space; and the use of rockets, satellites, and other space probes to get information directly from space. Students can be helped to consider the impact of these modern developments upon our general view of the nature of the universe and the solar system.

b. Biology students should become familiar with the newer findings in genetics. For example, they should become aware of the fact that the genetic structure of bacteria can be modified by introducing DNA into the culture medium and by the transfer of genetic material from other bacteria by viruses (transformation-transduction). They should discuss the implications of this and other new findings for the theories of heredity.

c. Modern biology reaches into the macromolecular level of life organization. Modern biology teaching should do likewise. This calls for excursions into areas of organic chemistry. For example, in the study of heredity the academically talented student should be exposed not only to the findings of Mendel, Morgan, and Muller, but also to those of Beadle, Tatum, Lederberg, and Zinder, who in recent years have opened up the field of chemical genetics. To prepare students for these excursions into areas of organic chemistry, structural formulas should be introduced in the study of nutrition and digestion. Certain configurations of elements, such as acid groups, amino groups, and the benzene ring, should become as familiar as water and carbon dioxide.

Students should understand such terms as polymerization, hydrolysis, and organic catalyst.

d. Since the turn of the century the physical sciences have been fundamentally altered by the development of atomic and nuclear theories, relativity, and the concepts of wave mechanics. These developments provide insights into classical science which should be absorbed into the secondary-school curriculum, rather than simply tacked onto the end of a single course. The experimental program being developed by the Physical Science Study Committee provides one example of how this might be done. Traditional subjects are introduced, with the eventual exploration of wave-particle duality in mind. Thus wave phenomena in classical physics are studied at great length, so that the student is prepared for a study of modern physics from the wave-mechanics approach.

Guideline 2

Content areas should be developed in depth. To this end, a few well-chosen areas should be studied, and the emphasis should be on better quality of teaching and learning rather than on covering a great diversity of subject matter. Tone and character are more desirable than covering many areas.

a. The development of areas of science in depth makes possible better quality experiences in science for students in grades seven, eight, and nine. For example, in the study of the universe and solar system students will have a chance to get a picture of how man's concept of the nature of the universe has changed from a geocentric to a heliocentric concept of the solar system. Also, students will have more opportunity for first-hand field and laboratory experiences, such as the observation and charting of stars, constellations, and man-made satellites. They will make greater use of such scientific material and apparatus as sky charts, telescopes, and spectroscopes. They will gain an understanding of the scientific principles on which such instruments are based, and teachers will work through carefully selected problems, using approaches that are characteristic of a wide range of sciences. As a result of study in depth, students will better develop broad general concepts, such as those relating to the nature of the universe and the solar system, of the nature and origin of light and other electromagnetic radiations.

b. The study of weather phenomena should include modern theories concerning the basic causes of weather. Current evidence of vast changes in the earth's weather, the influence on weather of the arctic and antarctic ice caps, the implications of our new knowledge concerning ocean currents, recent research dealing with the development of rain and other forms of precipitation, the possible effects of changes in the carbon dioxide content of the atmosphere on the earth's heat balance, and other aspects of current thinking about the weather should help pupils understand the complex interplay of forces that determine our weather.

c. New tools, such as seismic sounding, are showing that the least explored continent, Antarctica, probably consists of a group of islands linked only by the overlying mass of ice. The study of polar weather, of which a record is preserved in ice layers, is giving profoundly important insights into world weather that have contributed, along with new information about the oceans, to the development of new theories accounting for the successive glacial and interglacial periods characteristic of the past million years. Further studies suggested by the new data and theories may enable us to anticipate major changes in world climate likely to come during the next decades and centuries and even raise the possibility of finding feasible ways to modify these changes. New small-scale model systems permit experimentation to test theories of cloud formation, atmospheric circulation, and storm structure; new mathematical analyses are helping us to elaborate improved theory; and computer

17

techniques are making possible the handling of immense amounts of data. Intensive exploration of the oceans is giving us for the first time at least the outlines of the major topographical features of the ocean basins and the pattern of deep currents beneath the previously known surface currents. Probing of the ocean bottom in the Southwest Pacific has revealed immense deposits of certain metallic ores which may supply the world's needs when ore bodies of the kind now being mined are exhausted.

d. Biological classification can begin with the recognition that all species have names and identifiable characteristics. On the basis of common characteristics, species are grouped into larger categories. By experiencing the naming, describing, and grouping of a series of geometrical figures and a random sampling of objects, students can approach taxonomy systematically and in depth. Inherent in the study of classification of living things is recognition of morphological, physiological, cytogenetic, and distributional characteristics of organisms; recognition of groups and species as changing systems; and a view of phylogeny in terms of evolution.

In studying the life cycle of fruit flies and water bugs, students can observe not only the stage of development but can carry out their own research with laboratory breeding populations. Further exercises may be conducted with fly larvae to demonstrate the hormonal control of metamorphosis.[3]

e. In the study of blood, the class can consider not only the phenomenon of agglutination under the influence of antisera A, B, M, N, and Rh, but can go on to see that, theoretically, there is practically an unlimited number of other antisera and that a person's blood is as

[3] Paulson, Richard, and others. *Laboratory and Field Studies in Biology: A Sourcebook for Secondary Schools.* (Produced by a high-school and college biology teachers conference under a grant from the National Science Foundation, 1958. A preliminary draft of this report has been distributed, and the report will be published early in 1960.)

unique as his fingerprints. Moreover, members of the class can consider the applications of serology in the identification of ultramicroscopic quantities of substances which defy analysis by chemical means and can study the applications of serology to evolution (phylogenetic relationships) and anthropology (human migrations). The phenomena associated with immunity and allergy can be brought into the same general picture. In brief, the study in depth of serum can be used to synthesize a great many otherwise disparate areas of biology.

f. In a discussion of energy exchange as a characteristic of chemical change, a class can go more deeply into the generalization that chemical reactions are either exothermic or endothermic. This may lead to a distinction between energy of activation and the energy absorbed or liberated by reaction. A discussion of energy of activation may lead to a study of its relationship to the disruption of chemical bonds that follow.

After the student acquires some knowledge of the stability of compounds, it becomes possible for him to compare chemical stability with values given in tables for heats of formation. The halides furnish excellent opportunities for such study. Students can design and carry out experiments to determine quantitatively such values as heats of neutralization and to determine whether values obtained vary according to the base used.

Guideline 3

The over-all science program for the talented should be planned carefully to assure continuity of the program from the elementary school through college. There must be continuity through the elementary school, junior high-school, senior high-school, and college. Such articulation should avoid the needless repetition of subject matter. Such an integrated science program requires careful, coordinated planning.

a. In teaching electricity, various aspects of electricity

should doubtless be studied at different levels. In the elementary school the qualitative study of electrostatics and magnetism might be stressed. In grades seven, eight, and nine emphasis might be on the study of electric current in various types of circuits, while in the senior high-school it might be on the study of electromagnetic radiation.

b. Similarly, in the development of experiences in the study of reproduction and heredity various understandings may be emphasized at different levels. In the elementary school the emphasis could be placed on the study of means of reproduction such as seeds, eggs, and the birth of living offspring. In grades seven, eight, and nine the emphasis might be on reproduction as sexual or asexual; while, in biology, heredity, with a study of chromosomes, genes, dominant and recessive characteristics, and mutations, would be taught.

Guideline 4

Science content should be developed in such a way that pupils have many opportunities to work with science materials, equipment, and apparatus. They should have many laboratory experiences and other activities in which they are called upon to act and think like scientists and to attempt scientific approaches to the solution of problems. Pupils should come to understand the role of planned experimentation, observation, and recording of observation and data in the process of extending scientific knowledge and understandings. They should have opportunities to experience the joy of discovery.

a. In the seventh, eighth, and ninth grades students should have a chance to handle the materials, equipment, and apparatus of science. For example, in the study of series and parallel circuits it is not enough to describe these circuits. Students should wire bulbs or other electrical appliances into circuits and use meters and simple calculations to discover the nature of each kind of circuit.

b. In high-school biology foods may be tested for their vitamin C content by using the chemical indicator, indophenol (2, 6 dichlorophenol indophenol). After students have seen that ascorbic acid will decolorize the blue indicator, they may try various dilutions of ascorbic acid to discover that the test may be made quantitative as well as qualitative. Later they may measure the relative vitamin C content of various fruit juices and juices pressed from other foods.

c. Many so-called "open-ended" experiments are now available in the area of chemistry.[4] When mercuric oxide is used in connection with a discussion of Priestley's discovery of oxygen, students commonly generalize incorrectly that oxides as a group are unstable. One open-ended experiment raises the question, "Do oxides, as a class, release oxygen when heated?" If a variety of oxides and common laboratory apparatus are available, students can easily find the answers to the question.

Guideline 5

The choice and development of content areas should be planned to reveal the relationships among the sciences. Pupils should learn how investigation in any one area of science draws upon the knowledge and ideas developed in other science areas.

A group of science-talented students may engage in a project studying the uptake of radioactive phosphorus by fresh-water algae. In relation to this project they would learn the use of the Geiger counter and radioactive isotopes in medicine, industry, and research, using materials producing less than 10 microcuries of radioactivity. They may investigate the possibility of utilizing algae to rid streams of radioactivity. In addition, they may test the effect of various agents in removing radioactive phosphorus. Thus the disciplines of biology, chemistry, and physics may be employed in

---

[4] Manufacturing Chemists Association. *Scientific Experiments in Chemistry*. Washington, D. C.: the Association, 1958.

relation to a significant problem. They may see how a knowledge of radioactivity and the use of radioisotopes have contributed to advances in fields of science ranging from anthropology to zoology. If the students are led to an understanding of how developments in one science can be used advantageously in other sciences, they will have learned one of the most important lessons of science.

Guideline 6

The science program should be planned for the early and increasing application of mathematics to the precise formulation of scientific relationships and to the application of scientific laws and principles. The pupil should acquire an appreciation of the order and clarity that the use of mathematical methods brings to the organization and application of science. Working skills would include the use of the slide rule and of logarithms.

a. Seventh-, eighth-, and ninth-grade students should handle some kinds of data in quantitative terms. For example, youngsters of this age can learn to use such relationships as Ohm's Law. Ammeters and voltmeters can be employed in obtaining data, which can be interpreted and used through the application of Ohm's Law.

b. By introducing the mathematics of probability in illustrating the Mendelian Law of Segregation, the teacher more clearly describes the events of inheritance than in only pictorially demonstrating segregation. When first understandings of genetics are quantitative, the process of enlarging the concepts of genetics is facilitated by phenolthiocarbamide (PTC) taste-testing in families and sample populations. Students can describe the genotypes, mathematically determine the frequencies of tasting and nontasting genes, and test the laws governing the elimination of a recessive gene from a population.

c. The development of physical concepts depends upon mathematical reasoning. Not only can principles be formulated with great precision, but many ideas in the sciences are fundamentally mathematical. The student can profitably study functioning relationships in algebra, such as inverse square laws. This relationship permits one to study gravitational forces, magnetic forces, electrostatic forces, and also the manner in which radiation decreases in intensity with distance from a source.

Guideline 7

The teaching of science should be concentrated increasingly on the development of the concepts, principles, broad generalizations, and great issues of science rather than on the accumulation of unrelated facts. Many applications drawn from the pupil's environment and direct experiences should serve to clarify and illustrate the functioning of these concepts, principles, and generalizations.

a. The general principle of conservation of mass and energy is fundamental to the sciences. It may be taught on many levels. The junior high-school student may profitably study conservation of mass in chemical reactions involved in the burning of a candle or a photographic flashbulb. As the able student matures, he may study conservation of mechanical energy in simple machines or in the motion of a pendulum. This study can lead into an examination of other forms of energy— heat in a machine with friction or electrical and chemical in the case of a charging battery. It can eventually provide a means for examining Einstein's theory of the relationship between mass and energy. This may be studied from various viewpoints: the consequences of an atomic explosion, the means for understanding nuclear reactions, and the philosophical significance of the development of one or two limited conservation laws into a powerful unifying principle in the sciences.

b. That a living organism can be understood only in association with its physical and biotic environment is a fundamental principle of biology. In the lower grades, the principle can be applied to interpretations of the functions of the beaks and feet of birds; the limbs, body covering, and teeth of mammals; and the contours of fishes. In the high-school grades, the principle can be extended in terms of the nitrogen and carbon cycles, trace elements, and such biotic relationships as commensalism, symbiosis, and parasitism.

c. An even greater synthesizing principle in biology is represented by the concept of evolution. Students taking earth science in junior high-school might well consider the variety of fossils in sedimentary rock and how the ages of the fossils are determined. In high-school biology, anatomical, embryological, and other facts support an interpretation not only of the fossils, but of existing organisms. It is conceivable that at least some academically talented students might even be led to consider some of the recent researches in biochemistry that fall in line with the concept of evolution.[5]

Guideline 8

Full advantage should be taken of the science resources of the community for enriching and supplementing the science program for talented students.

The community affords a wealth of opportunity for enriching and supplementing a science program for talented students. Resource people drawn from local industry, science research laboratories, colleges and universities, engineering, and government agencies may be invited to speak to student groups, to furnish relevant literature, to perform demonstrations, and to use illustrative aids. Students may be apprenticed to local scientists to learn basic research techniques and the use of scientific materials. Local museums, zoos, and botanic gardens have varied resources and highly trained staffs that may be utilized in school science programs.

---

[5] Wald, George. "The Significance of Vertebrate Metamorphosis." *Science* 128: 1481; December 1958.

Natural areas near the school may be investigated to determine ecological relationships among living things and geological phenomena, such as the effects of weathering, erosion, and stratification.

Guideline 9

Science should be taught in such a way as to reveal the influence of science in such other areas of culture as politics, economics, world outlook, standard of living, and the influence of these areas in the development of science. Recognition of the social responsibility of science should be developed.

a. In biology the study of conservation should be aimed at a realization that the resolution of our conflict with the U.S.S.R. is based on the supply of our natural resources (soil, water, food, and human health) as well as our missile and atomic warhead firing power. In dealing with the topics of genetics and evolution, the teacher should not overlook such related social problems as radioactive fallout from the explosion of atomic bombs, the problem of overpopulation in the face of underproduction of food, the eugenic and euthenic effects of war, farm parity, and tariff regulations.

b. In chemistry demands for better fuels resulted in the science of petroleum chemistry and led to many new drugs, dyes, plastics, and explosives as by-products of this research. In turn, these products have caused many changes in our way of living and have paved the way to still further discoveries.

c. In physics the study of the development of nuclear energy should lead to an investigation of the implications of this new energy source for world peace, for the moral responsibilities of world leadership, for the improvement of the standard of living of the world's peoples, and for literature and other forms of creative art which will interpret these ideals.

Methods for Teaching the Academically Talented Science Student

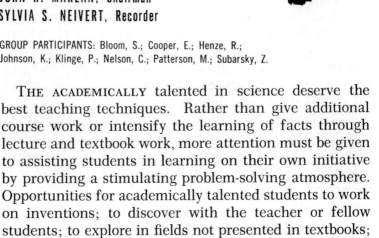

JOHN H. MAREAN, Chairman
SYLVIA S. NEIVERT, Recorder

GROUP PARTICIPANTS: Bloom, S.; Cooper, E.; Henze, R.;
Johnson, K.; Klinge, P.; Nelson, C.; Patterson, M.; Subarsky, Z.

THE ACADEMICALLY talented in science deserve the best teaching techniques. Rather than give additional course work or intensify the learning of facts through lecture and textbook work, more attention must be given to assisting students in learning on their own initiative by providing a stimulating problem-solving atmosphere. Opportunities for academically talented students to work on inventions; to discover with the teacher or fellow students; to explore in fields not presented in textbooks; yes, even the opportunity to succeed or fail in some research project must be provided. The teacher should be counselor and co-planner with these students, not their supervisor.

Teachers of academically talented students have found a great variety of methods effective in teaching this group of students. Donaldson confirmed this in a recent survey and indicated that the value in most methods lies in placing responsibility on the individual student.[6]

Suggestions for inclass activities for the talented may be grouped under the following three general headings: *reading, doing,* and *reporting.*

1. Reading

The accomplishments of the academically talented student will be based on knowledge and interests gained

---

[6] Donaldson, Robert R. *A Study of Methods for Teaching Rapid Learners in Secondary School Science.* Unpublished doctor's thesis. Ithaca, N. Y.: Cornell University, 1955.

through extensive and intensive reading of the literature of science.

An understanding of the nature of a scientific theory should be developed by the student's tracing the development of representative classical theories in the history of science. This will give the student reason and opportunity to read from original classical literature. Obviously, the importance of adequate library facilities for these students cannot be overemphasized.[7]

The Harvard Case Studies are examples of materials which can provide insight into the background, environment, and conditions which influenced the scientists in their theorizing and experimentation. Reading from the history of science and from original literature should help the student to realize that the theories, principles, and laws of science are the product of human intuition, ingenuity, experiment, and industry.

In biology, for example: after providing an appropriate background, including the structure of the pea blossom and of variations in pea plants, the teacher could have the class read excerpts of Gregor Mendel's *Experiments in Plant Hybridization* up to and including the data for the F_2 generation of monohybrids. The class should then be challenged to come up with an explanation of the remarkable consistency of the seven experiments described.

In chemistry: John Dalton's diagrams of elements and their weights as given in his *A New System of Chemical Philosophy* might be presented to the students. After examining his data for the weights of elements in CO and CO_2, the class should be challenged to devise a theory to explain the facts.

It is a truism that a science textbook is out of date by the time it reaches the classroom. But how many times are high-school library shelves filled with college text-

[7] See: Barnes, Cyrus D., and others. "Criteria for Selecting Supplementary Reading Science Books for Intellectually Gifted High School Students." *Science Education* 40: 215-18; April 1958.

books 10, 20, and even 30 years old! Certainly, the seventh grade it not too low a level for the student to become skilled in using the *Reader's Guide to Periodical Literature*. An intelligent use of the file catalogue is another asset for the academically talented student. Once he has developed these bibliographic skills, the talented science student will be able to spend leisure hours in building an understanding of the nature of scientific theory; he will be able to move then from his original interest to related interests.

It is also necessary that the school library be provided with periodicals appropriate for his reading and intellectual ability. A minimum selection would include: *Science Digest, Scientific American, Journal of the American Chemical Society, Natural History Magazine, Science World, Tomorrow's Scientists,* and *Science.*

Neither the classroom library nor the school library will be adequate for the bibliographic research of the academically talented student. Such large libraries as the New York Public Library and the John Crerar Library in Chicago are familiar with requests from interested high-school students. If prior arrangements are made, industrial and college libraries often make their resources available.

Reading skills of the academically talented are not always equivalent to their other academic abilities. The deficiency may be in speed, comprehension, vocabulary, or some other aspect of reading. In many high-schools remedial-reading help is available for all students. The already high attainment of the academically talented with defective reading habits can be increased by uncovering the reading handicap and remedying it.

Reading skills which the academically talented should develop include analysis of graphs, maps, and statistical tables. The academically talented student should be introduced at an early age to such references as handbooks of chemistry and physics and to the standard references for identification of plants and animals. The prominence of statistical techniques in today's research underscores the importance of a tie-in of science and mathematics programs for the academically talented student if he is to be literate in science.

2. *Doing*

Solving problems of the student-teacher planned type, which often have their origin in the reading and recitation periods of science study (or in outside activities), requires time over and above that provided for other academic classes. Double period combinations for laboratory by the academically talented students growing out of the development of original problems are imperative. Where administratively possible, five double periods per week are strongly recommended. (In some cases, triple periods may be both desirable and feasible.) Certainly, a minimum of one such double period per week is administratively possible in all school organizations where academically talented students are found.

Supervision of laboratory work requires more teacher time and planning than does a regular recitative period. A reduced class load per teacher seems inevitable. Time also must be made available for maintaining equipment and for preparing laboratory work. Often it is necessary to provide assistance for the teacher by establishing a system of paid laboratory assistants, which will be discussed at greater length in the section on "The Teacher of the Academically Talented Science Student."

Laboratory work for the academically talented student should be of the creative, problem-solving type, and, in the course of it, the student should experience a sense of discovery.

Examples of laboratory work illustrative of this approach are to be found in the field of chemistry.[8] For example, the "Estimation of Vitamin C in Fruit Juices"

---

[8] Manufacturing Chemists Association. *op. cit.*

gives a student no answers but permits him not only to explore the reaction of iodine with vitamin C, but to apply this reaction in determining the various vitamin C contents of juice under various conditions of preparation, storage, and preservation. He also learns to use the group procedure involved in problem solving, chemical equipment of a wide variety, and basic techniques. No blanks are available for students to supply a missing word; rather the student is required to think out all the ramifications of his work and to prepare a clear statement of what he found out instead of merely repeating old experiments, such as those demonstrating the allotropic forms of sulfur.

Many examples of problem-solving physics experiments are to be found among those recommended by the Physical Science Study Committee of the Massachusetts Institute of Technology. One such long-term laboratory assignment involves the construction of a ripple tank, various types of wave generators and stroboscopes, and the utilization of these devices in student determinations and discovery of frequency, wave length, and amplitude relationships. These devices can be applied further in the study of interference phenomena and focal length of lenses and in an exploration of little known details of wave motion inside lens systems. The powers of observation of the academically talented student can be challenged to a maximum under such conditions as offered by the kind of experiment described above. Many suggestions from students will grow out of this experiment for the improvement of equipment and for working together as small groups in the solution of problems.

Another committee has recommended the open-ended type of activities in the field of biology in order to provide a "more thorough and lasting knowledge of organisms and of scientific methods of inquiry. . . ."[9]

[9] Paulson, Richard, and others. *op. cit.*

The feeling of the group responsible for this publication was that laboratory work in biology should be done by "practicing the methods of science," not by merely following a cookbook procedure. For example, if the problem "How readily are minerals taken up in the fish skeleton?" is posed, background reading about radioactive materials should be provided, safety hazards and precautions explained, and the rest should be left up to the student—building a hypothesis, testing it, observing results, and drawing conclusions.

Some situations will indicate to the students that nothing can be proven by one trial, and it should be stressed that most experiments must be repeated many times. Indeed, the student should realize that statistically 499 is a *small* number. If it is not possible to use a large number of cases, the student should recognize the limitations of his research and should avoid drawing conclusions or claiming an accuracy which does not exist. To put it another way, the academically talented student should feel that, although his research project is an exceptional piece of work for a person of his age, its evaluation would be completely different in the light of the total amount of scientific knowledge.

The academically talented student should be led to a recognition of the fact that a suggested problem may either be unworthy or impossible of solution under existing conditions. However, he should understand that many seemingly trivial problems may have solutions which have far-reaching importance and that many seemingly impossible problems have yielded solutions to relatively simple but ingenious investigations.

3. Reporting

The academically talented student above all others *must* be able to communicate. Seminar-research courses especially offer opportunity for oral reporting. In addition, science clubs for the able science student should devote a large part of their time to this important activity. In reporting, the student should exhibit a thorough knowledge of the literature related to his own project. To be altogether ethical, he must give credit for his indebtedness to other researchers, to assistance from his teacher- or scientist-sponsor, and to those who have loaned him needed equipment or supplied materials.

The value of the seminar class or science club for the able science student lies in the fact that they (a) offer opportunity for clarification of the student's problems in the presentation of these problems to the class and (b) provide for the refinement of the research plan by suggestions and criticism from peers. With proper planning, regular science classes, although not as suitable as seminars and clubs, also offer opportunities for the academically talented student reporting on bibliographic and laboratory research.

The written reporting by the academically talented student should receive special emphasis, and he should be gaining these skills as he learns to become a scientist. A direct tie-in between science and English departments would be mutually beneficial. High-school science majors should be learning how to write the kinds of reports that will be later required of them on the job. English courses in composition might well devote some special attention to those interested in writing science reports or themes on science topics. In return, the science faculty could assist the English teachers by checking on the validity of the science content of the themes.

In addition, frequent progress reports on research problems should be made. Certainly, grading all these materials takes up much teacher time; but if the students are to acquire sufficient practice in writing, the teacher must perform the task and the time must be provided.

Reporting is directly linked with the reading aspect of research. During the reading stage, of course, a card-file system of annotating references should have been organized. An acceptable bibliographic method should have been mastered and consistently followed. In the reporting stage this skill should be used in setting up a sufficiently broad and up-to-date bibliography covering the area of the research problem. Footnoting and quotations should also follow an accepted standard.

Clarity and honesty must be stressed in reporting the individual project. Early in its pursuit, the problem should be stated concisely, with its limitations and delimitations. The methods should be outlined before the project is begun. The final report would include as its basis a clear statement of the problem and a detailed account of the methods followed, including statistical treatment of the data, results, and conclusions.

Evaluation

Before leaving the subject of inclass activities, a word should be said about grading. Student grades should not be such as to penalize the talented, especially in selected groups. Student performance, particularly in special groups, should be judged in relation to the entire student body. The teacher of the talented must strive constantly to maintain a proper perspective of what is truly the average of the student body. Classes of average students or ungrouped sections may provide this perspective. An average grade should be a warning to the talented student that he is performing below his ability. If a student in a special group is working to capacity but merits only an average grade, there is a real possibility that he has been improperly selected. In either case, he should be removed from this class before such a grade reaches his permanent record. Weighting the grades of those students in honors sections is sometimes used.

It has been found effective to informally notify students of their ranks relative to some standard, such as college achievement in a comparable subject. This, however, is only done orally, and to each student privately.

Suggested Activities and Resources

The following out-of-class activities and resources are among those which may be used in teaching the academically talented in science.

1. INDIVIDUAL AND SMALL GROUP PROJECTS. This type of activity goes beyond the regular class and laboratory activities. If there is to be time to complete long-term projects or series of related projects, then these should be started in the ninth or tenth grade. This means that identification and provision for the academically talented should occur before the junior high-school.

The term "discipline" is sometimes used to refer to an academic area. It implies that mastering that body of knowledge is a rigorous experience. This is true in science, and this fact should be learned early by those who are becoming scientists. The discipline of science includes extensive reading; careful planning; budgeting of time; meeting of deadlines; careful observing and recording of data; and other difficult, tedious, time-consuming activities. Projects worthy of the academically talented should be of this caliber, for these are not just the casual pursuits of a hobby.

Supervisory time and a place for carrying on these projects must be provided. If the laboratory is to be made available outside of school time, the supervising teacher must be compensated. It would be well to pay the science teacher for this type of activity rather than for collecting tickets at a football game, supervising lunchrooms or study halls, or keeping attendance records.

Plans for new building construction or remodeling of existing facilities should include project rooms with appropriate tools, work space, and storage facilities. This is the only way to insure that materials and projects are secure from tampering by other students, that project work can be carried on while the regular classrooms are occupied, and that projects can be left standing until they are completed. Darkrooms and greenhouses are now considered as standard facilities for teaching high-school science and should be included. Two recent reports on facilities for teaching science include descriptions of science-project rooms.[10] In addition there are several references which suggest projects and the methods for carrying them out.[11]

2. SEMINARS AND CLUBS. Although regular science classes may use the seminar approach in certain units several times a year, in some schools an undesignated seminar-type program is offered in the upper grades for students with varied science interests. This may be particularly valuable in breaking down arbitrary divisions among the sciences and in bringing together ideas from the biological and physical sciences. Individual student projects are frequently, though not necessarily, discussed in such seminars. In many of these seminars students have the opportunity to meet and talk with practicing scientists.

In many localities of the United States interested scientists, engineers, and mathematicians have organized

[10] National Science Teachers Association. *School Facilities for Science Instruction.* Washington, D. C.: the Association, a Department of the National Education Association, 1954.

National Science Teachers Association. *Action for Science Under NDEA.* Washington, D. C.: the Association, a Department of the National Education Association, 1959.

[11] National Science Teachers Association. *If You Want To Do a Science Project.* Washington, D. C.: the Association, a Department of the National Education Association, 1955.

National Science Teachers Association. *Student Projects.* (Revised edition.) Washington, D. C.: the Association, a Department of the National Education Association, 1958.

Science Service. *Thousands of Science Projects.* Washington, D. C.: the Service, 1953.

Goldstein, Philip. *How To Do an Experiment.* New York: Harcourt, Brace and Company, 1957.

themselves to provide evening and/or Saturday programs of lectures and individual project help for interested high-school students. Sometimes these programs are in cooperation with the high-school science programs; in other instances they bear no relationship or responsibility to the school program.

Under one plan the Rochester (New York) Council of Scientific Societies sponsors an extensive program of aid for science teachers and students. The Council is made up of representatives from more than 15 scientific societies. Working closely with the schools, it provides speakers, school science consultants, exhibits, tours, and open-house programs in university and industrial laboratories; and working closely with the Science Teachers Association of New York State, it sponsors an annual Science Congress.

The Joe Berg Foundation plan is another method by which scientists furnish help to able high-school science students. The Foundation acts as a liaison between the schools and interested industrial scientists and is prepared to offer suggestions for setting up seminar programs during the regular school day or in out-of-school hours.

For the science-talented youth, however, the emphasis should be on the "science" rather than the "club." Here is the chance for this student to report his research and to receive guidance and stimulation. The fine academic record of many science club members attests to the value of this opportunity.

In some schools, letters are awarded for academic attainment as well as athletic accomplishment. In accord with this focus on the academic side of secondary-school life, some science clubs are actually honor societies basing their membership on a certain high scholastic average.

3. SCIENCE COMPETITIONS. There is a great variety of science competitions, ranging from one requiring the

entrant to prepare a brief essay to one requiring him to take a test covering the field of science, conduct a project, and prepare a written report on that project. Some competitions are limited to one school or even a single class; others are nationwide. In some of these competitions a project or report whipped up a week before may win a prize; in others, many of the entries are of high quality.

Most significant among the science talent competitions are the Westinghouse Science Talent Search conducted by Science Service and the Science Achievement Awards Program of the Future Scientists of America Foundation of the National Science Teachers Association. The former is for high-school seniors and involves a test of scientific information as well as a project. The latter is to be recommended because of its developmental nature within three divisions: (a) seventh and eighth grades, (b) ninth and tenth, and (c) eleventh and twelfth.

4. MATERIALS ON LOAN. Local industries, colleges, and individuals will frequently lend materials to students or to the school for special research. These sources, including governmental agencies, are often willing to give, or sell at a fraction of their value, equipment and material. Physicians and laboratory technicians who have to replace investigative or therapeutic devices with later models may donate the former equipment. Industrial organizations can seldom afford to pack, transport, or sell many expendable materials if they move or remodel and, therefore, they make them available to schools. Military and other governmental agencies are constantly releasing equipment, instruments, and supplies to tax-supported institutions. A complete listing of the state agencies responsible for the distribution of surplus property may well be a starting point for securing such materials.

5. UNIVERSITY SUMMER PROGRAMS. Long-established summer programs for high-school students on university

campuses, such as those of Northwestern, Indiana, Florida State, and Kansas, have recently been substantially supplemented by programs sponsored by local industry and foundation programs, particularly the National Science Foundation. Judicious selection is important and any program which threatens to exploit the student is to be avoided, but much learning and inspiration can result. University summer bulletins and special announcements should be consulted. The National Science Foundation, Washington 25, D. C., also provides information on programs for high-school students. To date, these are generally directed toward students in the tenth, eleventh, and twelfth grades.

University courses are a possibility in the event that no advanced placement program is available. Students may frequently take college courses during summer or by special arrangement during the school year. If they subsequently matriculate, credit may be given for this work. Examples are provided by the University of Rochester (New York) and The University of Texas. Obviously any listing would be incomplete and of little value. Interested teachers, therefore, should check with nearby institutions.

6. SPECIAL SUMMER PROGRAMS IN THE REGULAR SCHOOL. Classes which offer outstanding students increased opportunity for enriched or expanded study during the summer months have been replacing remedial courses in the regular school. Some programs are sponsored by the school alone, whereas others have received outside support. Special project sessions are available in some places while advanced academic study is offered elsewhere. The program is too widespread to list all sources of information. An example of one academic program is that offered at Archbold, Ohio and an example of projects for summer sessions is that carried on in the San Bernardino (California) city schools.

7. SCIENCE CAMPS AND SUMMER EMPLOYMENT OPPORTUNITIES. Both of these activities are growing in popu-

larity, particularly in nature study and the natural sciences.[12] Such a program is presently conducted at Kansas State University.

Talented students may find part-time and summertime employment as assistants in college, industrial, or government research laboratories, such as the National Institutes of Health, the Robert A. Taft Engineering Center, and Argonne Laboratory. The National Bureau of Standards is one of a number of agencies offering opportunities for research employment to qualified students. In local industry or colleges such programs might be developed if they are not already in existence. Such a program is a very desirable extension of the one-to-one working relationship suggested by Mark Hopkins. Sections of scientific societies in the community may be of assistance in locating employment for interested students.

Similar to the opportunity described above but affording less financial reward are such programs as those offered by the Woods Hole Marine Biology Laboratory in Massachusetts; the Jackson Memorial Laboratory, Bar Harbor, Maine; and the Worcester Foundation for Experimental Biology, Shrewsbury, Massachusetts.

8. CORRESPONDENCE COURSES IN MATHEMATICS OR IN SCIENCE TECHNOLOGY. Because laboratory experience is considered indispensable in learning science, some activity other than study from texts is considered necessary. However, correspondence courses from reliable schools are frequently excellent. This is one method of self-study which may be effective.

Once more, it is well to remember that this list is incomplete. The resourcefulness mentioned earlier that is expected of a competent teacher by both his students and his administrators will be most helpful in the design

---

[12] The President's Committee on Scientists and Engineers. *Summer Programs for High School Students.* Washington, D. C.: the Committee, 1958.

and implementation of activities for these outstanding students. But in no way should this imply that the mere assignment of more work or of relatively meaningless projects will give even lip-service to the needs of these students. Keynotes to the elements of such a program must be *quality of work and growth* toward valuable and realistic scientific practices.

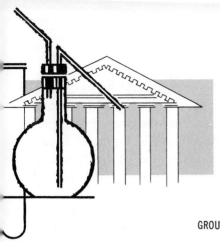

The Teacher of the Academically Talented Science Student

GEORGE E. MATHES, Chairman

DONALD B. SUMMERS, Recorder

GROUP PARTICIPANTS: Condon, M.; Johnson, P.;
Leisner, R.; Rutledge, J.; Summers, D.

FOR MANY years science teachers have been giving yeoman service to the education of youth of all abilities—low, average, and high—all in one class. Now, with the recognition by the public of the waste of the most valuable asset, high mental ability, a new emphasis must be given to the education of the academically talented. Science teachers are called upon to assume the grave responsibility for educating these students to meet the challenges of the world of today and of the future.

It is recognized that in some small schools the students of high ability may be few in number and must be taught in heterogeneous classes. This is no less a challenge than that of teaching a group composed entirely of more able students. The talented student deserves stimulating teaching in no matter what educational situation he finds himself.

The Training of the Teacher

HE SHOULD HAVE A COMPREHENSIVE BACKGROUND. A well-educated teacher should have a deep appreciation of the interlocking facets of knowledge so that he can reveal these areas and their relationships to the gifted science student.

This background of education, ideally, would include the humanities: English, social studies, philosophy, a modern foreign language, art, and music. The science

41

teacher must have the ability to speak and write clearly and succinctly. He should be familiar with the central facts and issues of history and economies, and his appreciation of art, music, and the classics should add, not only to his own background, but also to his cultural contacts with students. This is the background expected of all teachers.

HE SHOULD BE SPECIALIZED IN HIS FIELD OF INSTRUCTION. The teacher of the gifted should possess sufficient general knowledge to recognize the interrelations of the various branches of science and the absence of definite boundaries among them. Naturally, some knowledge of the major areas of science is desirable, but it is assumed that the teacher will specialize in one of them.

The studies in chemistry should provide for preparation in general inorganic chemistry, organic chemistry, analytical chemistry, and biochemistry. The teacher specializing in chemistry would also take considerable work in physical chemistry and would become informed about research techniques, equipment, and design.

The studies in physics should include general physics and biophysics, or the equivalent. The teacher who specializes in physics should have further training in electricity and magnetism, optics, thermodynamics, mechanics, atomic physics, and nuclear physics.

The studies for the specialist in earth science should include work related to the solar system and the sidereal universe; the study of weather systems, structural geology, and soil science.

The studies in biological science should include botany, zoology (vertebrate and invertebrate), microbiology, and field study. A teacher who specializes in this area would seek preparation in such fields as embryology, genetics, plant and animal physiology, anatomy, and morphology. Acquaintance with research techniques, equipment, and design are necessary for the specialist in this area; but it is to be hoped that the science teacher specializing in another aspect of science may also gain some acquaintance with research during his general studies in the area of biology.

The preparation in mathematics should provide a working knowledge of algebra, geometry, calculus, statistics, and probability. Some understanding of the mathematical basis for computers would be valuable. The teacher should be sufficiently familiar with the literature of mathematics to find help for himself and for his gifted students.

HE SHOULD HAVE AN ADEQUATE PROFESSIONAL EDUCATION. The teacher of the gifted student should have courses in education that will equip him to understand young people and the processes inherent in their thinking and learning. His preparation should include educational philosophy and psychology and methods of teaching. He should be familiar with the tests by which students' abilities are measured, their expectancy determined, and their achievement evaluated. In particular, the teacher of gifted students in science needs to have experience in teaching individuals or groups within a class who are working on special projects. He must be aware of the ways by which regular classwork may be enriched for the more able.

HE SHOULD KEEP UP TO DATE WITH SCIENCE. All teachers need to keep abreast of new knowledge in their special fields. This is of vital importance for the science teacher because of today's rapid developments, some of which are outdated almost as soon as they are announced. Other sections of this report stress the need for an adequate library of science reference books and current periodicals; this is a necessary facility for the teacher in carrying forward his day-by-day growth in subject-matter competence.

He should take advantage of institutes sponsored during the academic year and during the summer months by such private and government agencies as the National Science Foundation, Oak Ridge Institute of Nuclear Studies, the Shell Companies Foundation, the I. E.

du Pont de Nemours, and other companies. Scientific and professional writing is another means of becoming acquainted with new developments. Summer programs devoted to curriculum construction are rewarding ways of learning about the latest research in science teaching.

One method for keeping up to date is participation in the activities of local, state, and national scientific and professional societies; preparation of papers and attendance at their sessions to hear the papers and discussions of others are valuable experiences.

The opportunities for grants to facilitate research studies in science during the school year are worthy of special attention. Teachers have an opportunity to carry forward continuous studies near the developing scientific frontier. The opportunity to include gifted students in phases of such studies is especially challenging.

HE SHOULD BE A STUDENT OF TEACHING. A teacher should have had enough varied experience in the classroom to have many resources upon which to draw. He should have developed standards for achievement. He must be sensitive to his pupils' learning problems and able to adapt the classwork to individual needs. Above all, the teacher should be able to ignite that spark of interest which transforms any classroom into a vital experience in the lives of boys and girls.

HE SHOULD HAVE WORK OR RESEARCH EXPERIENCE IN SCIENTIFIC FIELDS. Several types of on-the-job research activities which have been carried on have already been cited. This form of work experience has long been accepted for college teachers. The same opportunities for secondary-school teachers of gifted students would provide for growth in subject-matter competence and laboratory skills, not to mention the remuneration so highly cherished by college teachers.

Summer work in an industry would give the teacher of the gifted a chance to acquire vivid illustrations and useful know-how. Furthermore, acquaintance with industrial personnel may pay high dividends for the school when technical persons are solicited to provide special help for gifted students. People in industry can help the teacher by making available some useful but obsolete equipment to the science department. Industrial personnel can also become acquainted with the problems of education in general and can aid the science teacher through proper communication with the board of education.

A summer devoted to participation in research can provide education, recognition, and remuneration to the teacher of the gifted. Such work may reveal research problems suitable for gifted students, and at the same time it may help to identify college staff members who would serve as consultants in schools that could profit from their services. Recent offerings of research assistantships cover a variety of fields including agriculture, atomic energy, cancer research, and genetics in colleges, universities, industrial, and government laboratories in all parts of the country.

Although plant visitation can help the teacher in keeping up to date, the tour itself is likely to stress technology rather than the basic science so important for bright students. Even so, it is of value in keeping the teacher informed about the applications of science and is a way of providing useful illustrations for the classroom. It might also increase the teacher's contacts with persons who could provide consultative and other help to the schools.

The Personal Characteristics of the Teacher

HE SHOULD BE AN INTERESTED COUNSELOR. Obviously, any teacher of the gifted must have all of the attributes of a good teacher—at the elementary, secondary, or collegiate level, no matter whether the subject be in the arts, sciences, or humanities. Such a teacher needs other special qualities, for he is dealing with students who have special needs. First, he should have a deep interest in his students as persons. This is true whether he is teaching a class or only a few individuals. In working with those of high ability, the teacher should guide and counsel them as they discover their special interests and competencies. He should help them to realize their obligation to use these abilities to advantage.

A second, vitally important quality is the teacher's ability to instill in his students a devotion to the methods and content of science and to challenge them intellectually. He should develop in them the habit of approaching all study so that they recognize problems, define purposes, plan methods of attack, use available resources, draw conclusions, and evaluate results.

A third essential is the willingness to give cheerfully of his time and talents. This may mean extra hours, early or late, in the laboratory, conference, or classroom.

Fourth, the teacher of the talented must enjoy laboratory work and have a reasonable skill in the use of equipment. He must have the imagination to devise and the dexterity to design and create equipment with the materials at hand. He must have the patience to direct the student toward acquiring these skills themselves, rather than succumbing to an uncontrollable urge to do this work for them.

Last, the teacher of the talented must have the qualities necessary for establishing mutual relationships with nonteaching scientists. He must have an inquiring mind and respect, but not awe, for research and researchers. "I don't know, but let's find out," must be a part of his everyday vocabulary.

HE SHOULD BE A MEMBER OF THE SCHOOL SOCIETY. The teacher of the talented must recognize that he is a member of a working team dedicated to the total educational growth of all boys and girls, whether they be the less able, average, talented, or gifted. He also recognizes that other subject-matter areas are essential to the total educational experience of the student. This attitude must be reflected in his contacts and his cooperation with students, teachers, and the administrators of the school.

46

He should be a professional person. This teacher should be an active member of the local, state, and national associations which are dedicated to the advancement of education as a profession. He should belong to and participate in the programs of the science teachers' associations, sharing the results of research with his colleagues throughout the country.

As a scientist, the teacher should be actively associated with the scientific society pertinent to his special field. Many of these groups have local chapters with which the teacher should be affiliated.

It is imperative that the teacher be responsive to the total community in which he serves and from which he derives his livelihood. He should support the total school program and other community projects and concerns.

Special Facilities and Resources Needed by the Teacher

He should have necessary equipment and materials. In teaching the talented, specialized equipment and materials beyond those commonly used are often necessary. Depending upon the nature of student research projects, a wide variety of specialized items, not always expensive but often unusual, must be utilized. For purchasing these materials, a petty cash fund should be established so that these sums are readily available.

He may need the services of additional personnel. To free a teacher's time for maximum instructional contact with talented students, certain assistance should be provided. Competent, paid laboratory assistants may be drawn from the ranks of qualified members of the community, such as retired personnel, housewives, and college students, or from among qualified high-school students. Clerical help should be made available to handle such routine work for the science teacher as recording grades, typing stencils, and taking dictation. Trained teaching assistants could aid materially in reducing time spent by the teacher in such tasks as reading students' papers, selecting reference materials, and ordering supplies.

HE SHOULD HAVE A REASONABLE TEACHING LOAD. Class size for talented students probably should be limited to 15 or 20 students. The scheduled responsibilities of teachers of the talented should be adjusted to make them commensurate with the extra demands of such teaching.

HE SHOULD HAVE ADEQUATE LIBRARY FACILITIES. Reference books and periodicals should be available to the talented students in the classroom or laboratory. Additional reference books; scientific encyclopedias; supplementary books, such as those contained in the Traveling High School Library of the American Association for the Advancement of Science; and scientific periodicals should be available in a central library.

HE SHOULD HAVE FACILITIES FOR PROJECTS. Space should be set aside, preferably outside of the classroom or laboratory, in which work may be carried on by students and teacher on research projects. Here, projects in various degrees of completion may remain undisturbed by the regular class and laboratory activities. Hand tools and minor machine tools, such as a drill press and a bandsaw, should be available for use in fashioning wood and metal items needed in research projects. Photographic facilities, including a darkroom and associated equipment, are also necessary.

HE SHOULD HAVE CONFERENCE SPACE. An area offering reasonable privacy should be provided for interviews and consultations, as well as for study and meditation.

Obviously, these facilities will require more than the usual expenditure of funds for science. Increased funds, secured through an increase in the usual channels of school support or, in some cases, through additional support by local organizations or foundations, will be necessary to secure these conditions. The public must be informed of the need for obtaining additional funds to provide for the education of the talented.

A Program for Consideration

Robert R. Donaldson, Chairman of the Conference;
Charles E. Bish; Robert H. Carleton; Margaret J. McKibben.

THE CULTURAL climate of the mid-twentieth century has become so rich in scientific information that today's high-school student is quite a different person from his counterpart of 20 or even 10 years ago. Few junior high-school students today will be content with wiring a door-bell in general science or with making a collection of insects in biology. This is particularly true of the academically talented student.

The growing concern for a K-12 science program promises to yield rapid improvement in standards of science teaching at the earlier levels. Teachers are find-ing that much of the material formerly taught at the junior high-school level can successfully be included in elementary science programs. For these and other rea-sons, we are faced with an ultimatum to upgrade science teaching at the junior high-school level or to lose the interest of these youth through boredom.

While recognizing that it would be impossible to make a nationwide adoption of any science program for the academically talented, those planning the joint National Education Association-National Science Teachers Asso-ciation Conference on Providing for the Able Science Student offer the following suggestions as useful in shaping a program of secondary-school science for these students. These suggestions seem to us to fit the recom-mendations of the conference participants; our purpose in listing them is to crystallize some specific proposals which teachers, supervisors, and administrators may want to consider, to accept, to reject, or to use as a springboard in their own curriculum redesigns.

Seventh and Eighth Grades

For academically talented students, a good foundation in general science should be laid by the end of the eighth grade, especially if there is a good program of science experiences in the preceding elementary school grades. This means that seventh- and eighth-grade courses would "wrap up" the usual general science study of aspects of our environment and such socialized units as communication, transportation, and conservation. Indeed, the students should be well advanced in developing functional understanding of important principles of physical and biological science, such as those in the list by Smith.[13] Generous use of problem solving as a method of instruction and the study of fundamental principles in depth should characterize science study at these grade levels.

In other sections of this report, the importance of individual laboratory work in all science courses has been stressed. This is true of junior high general science as well as more advanced courses. This should provide experiences which lead to growth in ability to use the methods of science and the ability to manipulate commonly used laboratory equipment. While much "directed" laboratory activity will still be necessary, the students should have many opportunities to find puzzling or perplexing questions from which may be developed investigations or projects having the "find out for yourself" flavor of scientific investigation. Administrative provisions and encouragement should support such kinds of laboratory activities in grades seven and eight.

[13] Smith, Herbert F. *A Determination of Principles and Experiments Desirable for a Course in General Science at the Junior High School Level.* Doctor's thesis. Ann Arbor: University of Michigan, 1951. (Reviewed in: *Science Education* 25: 279-84, December 1951; 26:32-47, February 1952.)

Ninth Grade

For the academically talented, the ninth-grade science course may still have general education objectives, but it will certainly be more rigorous than the traditional ninth-grade general science course. Three alternatives seem to be receiving serious consideration today: (a) the development of an earth science course; (b) the development of a course stressing fundamentals of physical science; and (c) moving "standard biology" to the ninth grade. The question of which alternative to choose will be answered differently from place to place, depending on considerations such as available rooms and facilities, available staff and their competencies, community or area resources, and the strength of school and community philosophy and traditions. In any event, positive leadership must be exercised to provide challenging experiences for these students at a critical point in their intellectual growth.

If the subject chosen for placement at this level is biology, the principles of classification, the physiological basis of life, genetic variation, vertical and horizontal distribution of organisms, and ecological relationships are among the topics which might be considered for inclusion. If the course chosen is one in the fundamentals of physical science, the content will include those principles which will serve as the basis for further study in chemistry and/or physics. If the decision is favorable to earth science as the ninth-grade course, emphasis should be on earth science principles rather than on mere descriptive or factual materials. Guidance in the development of such a course is provided by Caldwell's study.[14] It should also be mentioned that if earth science is given in the ninth-grade, then the 10-12

---

[14] Caldwell, Loren T. *A Determination of Earth Science Principles for Inclusion in the Science Program of General Education in the Secondary School.* Doctor's thesis. Bloomington: Indiana University, 1953. (Referred to in *The Science Teacher,* 25: 337-41; October 1958.)

sequence probably should be biology, chemistry, and physics. In any case, the academically talented student will be ready for the more specialized study of science.

Tenth, Eleventh, and Twelfth Grades

Strong chemistry and physics courses are recommended as offerings in these grades to round out the three years of science comprising the continuous program of physics, chemistry, and biology recommended by the Conference on the Identification and Education of the Academically Talented Student.[15]

If the student has had first-year and intermediate algebra and geometry, and if he is currently taking trigonometry, he has had ample experience in mathematics for work with complex problems in chemistry and physics. Use of the slide rule, logarithm tables, and some knowledge of elementary statistics will facilitate this.

In chemistry, emphasis should be on atomic structure, bonding, periodic grouping of elements, oxydation-reduction reactions, modern concepts of acids and bases, organic and biochemistry, and the use of "open-ended" or investigative type laboratory activities.

The physics course should be one which places the emphasis on fundamental understandings, both traditional and modern, rather than on technology and the more spectacular applications. The Physical Science Study [16] will, of course, offer many suggestions for modernizing the physics course if, indeed, this program is not adopted in its entirety.

There may be considerable variation in twelfth-grade elective science courses for the academically talented, depending on what has been done in grades 9-11 and as well as on other considerations. The following are possibilities:

[15] Invitation Conference on the Academically Talented Secondary School Pupil. *op. cit.,* p. 111.

[16] Physical Science Study Committee. *op. cit.*

Advanced or specialized courses in the biological and physical sciences may be offered.

Science seminars or science research courses frequently meet the needs and challenge the capacities of the academically talented.

A course based on the Harvard Case Studies is another type of senior science course which has been found to have merit.

Courses providing for advanced placement at the college level have also been found to be effective.

The one or more electives offered in the twelfth-grade will depend, of course, upon the demand and, since subject-matter background is so important, upon the training and experience of the teachers.

APPENDIX I

As an amateur, I have done sufficient practice teaching to be convinced that much can be done by a knowledgeable person genuinely interested in both the subject and the persons being taught. I would encourage youngsters of all ages to experience nature scientifically; i.e., to observe phenomena directly, to measure them approximately, and to describe them simply—by physical concepts. To develop science teaching both in primary and secondary-schools becomes even more important as we now look at proposed revisions of college courses which will omit many elementary facts formerly included.

In this connection, I would recommend three principles for guidance in the construction of curricula. The first I will call the principle of genetic selection. It is important that we begin at the psychological, social, and intellectual levels of the student. In my own experiences I have had no definite idea as to whether the concepts I selected were particularly appropriate to the grades involved. What is obviously requisite is a systematic identification of scientific concepts by study groups consisting of scientists, educational psychologists, and practicing teachers—all working together.

Cultural integration is the second principle. Those of us who are parents may become depressed by the sometimes too chaotic mixing of history and geography, of literature and sociology. Nevertheless, compartmentalization barriers are often needlessly artificial and should ultimately be broken down to conform more to natural areas and boundaries of studies. Mathematics and science integrate quite naturally; they can be mutually helpful. One of the teachers in a third grade informed

---

* From the opening address, "Frontiers of Science Education," by Raymond J. Seeger, Deputy Assistant Director, National Science Foundation, at the Joint Conference on Providing for the Able Science Student, December 1958, Washington, D. C.

me that her youngsters had shown a greater interest in multiplication after having seen some of its usefulness in physical experiments. The chief difficulty to date has been our failure to treat science as an important subject in elementary curricula. Now that science is beginning to assume an educational role commensurate with its significance in our modern technological society, for the first time we can make proper use of this natural and mutually beneficial integration. From the standpoint of college physics, indeed, I am convinced that the most important need for entering students is not more and more, higher and higher mathematics, not even more scientific techniques and more modern physics, but rather an understanding of the application of some simple mathematics to some simple physical phenomena —what might appropriately be called mathematical science. This relationship above all else must be cultivated early. Archimedes still has much to teach beginning students of nature.

The third principle which I wish to emphasize for curricula selection is the principle of wholesome meaning. A healthy life must be a combination of physical, mental, social (moral), and spiritual values. Accordingly, a wholesome education must include all these elements in a coordinated manner. For growing youngsters, including the talented, it is not so important that we heighten their scientific experiences; even more, we must widen their general outlook! We should regard them not as competitive teams attempting to climb spectacular mountains of achievements, but rather as adventuresome individuals out to enjoy the expansive plateaus of learning. Comprehension which involves insight is far more significant than acquaintance which involves mere sight. In a recent book on *The Physicist's Conception of Nature*, Werner Heisenberg has likened a teacher to an illuminator of landscapes. He noted: "Very occasionally, an object that has come into our field of view will suddenly begin to shine in its own light, first dimly and vaguely, then even more brightly, until finally it will glow through our entire mind, spill over to other subjects and eventually become an important part of our own life."[1] Evidently, one must allow sufficient exposure time for such a process to start—and then a period of incubation. Education involves organic growth, not just material acquisition.

Physics can be fun for all ages, for all people, for the academically talented student as well as for the average young citizen! In his book on *Science, Theory, and Man,* Erwin Schrödinger once wrote in a chapter headed "Science, Art and Play": "The chief and lofty aim of science today as in every other age is the fact that it enhances the general joy of living . . . It is the duty of the teacher of science to impart to his listeners knowledge that will prove useful in their professions; but it should be his intense desire to do it in such a way as to cause them pleasure."[2] Let us enable our young people to enjoy their scientific environment! The sources of happiness in living are not so many that we dare deprive them of their rightful intellectual heritage.

APPENDIX II

CONFERENCE PARTICIPANTS

The following persons participated in the National Education Association-National Science Teachers Association Joint Conference on Providing for the Able Science Student, held December 4, 5, and 6, 1958, at the Roosevelt Hotel, Washington, D. C. Robert R. Donaldson was general chairman of the conference.

Bish, Charles E., Director, Project on the Academically Talented Student, National Education Association, 1201 Sixteenth Street, N. W., Washington 6, D. C.

---

[1] Heisenberg, Werner. *The Physicist's Conception of Nature.* New York: Harcourt, Brace and Company, 1958. p. 56.

[2] Schrödinger, Erwin. *Science, Theory, and Man.* New York: Dover Publications, Inc., 1957. p. 29.

Bloom, Samuel W., Head, Science Department, Monroe High School, Rochester 7, New York.

Brown, Annie Sue, Curriculum Specialist in Science, Board of Education, Atlanta, Georgia.

Condon, Mary M., Assistant Director, Division of Rural Service, National Education Association, 1201 Sixteenth Street, N. W., Washington 6, D.C.

Cooper, Edwin H., Science Teacher, Madison High School, Madison, New Jersey.

Cornell, Ruth E., Chairman, Secondary School Science Department, Wilmington Public Schools, 625 East Tenth Street, Wilmington, Delaware.

Donaldson, Robert R., Science Department, State University Teachers College, Plattsburgh, New York.

Henze, Robert E., Education Secretary, American Chemical Society, 1801 K Street, N. W., Washington, D. C.

Hess, Walter E., Associate Secretary, National Association of Secondary-School Principals, 1201 Sixteenth Street, N. W., Washington 6, D. C.

Jacobson, Willard J., Associate Professor of Natural Sciences, Teachers College, Columbia University, New York 27, New York.

Johnson, Keith C., Supervising Director of Science, District of Columbia Public Schools, Wormley Administration Building, Washington 7, D. C.

Johnson, Philip G., Professor of Science Education, 3 Stone Hall, Cornell University, Ithaca, New York.

Klinge, Paul, Coordinator for School Science, Indiana University, Bloomington.

Laster, Howard, Assistant Professor of Physics, University of Maryland, College Park.

Lawson, Chester A., Professor and Head, Department of Natural Science, Michigan State University, East Lansing.

Leisner, Robert S., Assistant to the Executive Director, American Institute of Biological Sciences, 2000 P Street, N. W., Washington 6, D. C.

Marean, John H., Physics Teacher, Reno High School, Reno, Nevada.

Mathes, George E., Director of Science, Denver Public Schools, Denver, Colorado.

McKibben, Margaret J., Assistant Executive Secretary, National Science Teachers Association, 1201 Sixteenth Street, N. W., Washington 6, D. C.

Metzner, Jerome, Chairman, Department of Introductory Science and Biology, Bronx High School of Science, 120 East 184th Street, Bronx 58, New York.

Neivert, Sylvia S., Head of Science Department, Bay Ridge High School, Brooklyn, New York.

Nelson, Clifford R., Coordinator for Junior High School Science, City of Newton School Department, Newton, Massachusetts.

Patterson, Margaret E., Consultant, Ford Foundation, New York, New York; Home address: 906 Gallatin Street, N. W., Washington 11, D. C.

Paulson, Richard E., Professional Assistant, Course Content Improvement Section, National Science Foundation, Washington 25, D. C.

Rutledge, James A., Associate Professor of Secondary Education, University of Nebraska, Lincoln.

Slesnick, Irwin L., Instructor, Department of School Experimentation, The Ohio State University, Columbus 10.

Subarsky, Zachariah, Coordinator of Special Science Activities, Bronx High School of Science, 120 East 184th Street, Bronx 58, New York.

Summers, Donald B., Professor of Chemistry, Glassboro State Teachers College, Glassboro, New Jersey.

Taffel, Alexander, Principal, Bronx High School of Science, 120 East 184th Street, Bronx 58, New York.

Tompkins, Ellsworth, Associate Secretary, National Association of Secondary-School Principals, 1201 Sixteenth Street, N. W., Washington 6, D. C.

Van Hooft, Gordon E., Chief, Bureau of Secondary Curriculum Development, New York State Department of Education, Albany.

Williams, Harry H., Vice Principal and Head of Science Department, Horace Mann School, 231 West 246th Street, New York, New York.

APPENDIX III

RESPONDENTS BY MAIL

These persons, although not present at the conference, contributed their experience by giving their viewpoints on six important issues in the education of the able high-school science student.

Boyer, Donald Allen, Science Education Consultant and Teacher, Winnetka Public Schools, Winnetka, Illinois.

Decker, Donald G., Director of Instruction, Colorado State College, Greeley.

Henderson, J. Donald, Associate Professor of Physics, University of North Dakota, Grand Forks.

Lingren, Vernon C., Professor of Education, School of Education, University of Pittsburgh, Pittsburgh, Pennsylvania.

Lowry, Nelson L., Dean, Arlington High School, Arlington Heights, Illinois.

Miller, Delmas, Principal, University High School, Morgantown, West Virginia.

Neal, Nathan A., Editor, McGraw-Hill Book Company, Inc., New York, New York.

Nelson, Clarence H., Office of Evaluation Services, Michigan State University, East Lansing.

Oppe, Greta, Head, Science Department, Ball High School, Galveston, Texas.

Owen, Mrs. Archie MacL., Supervisor of Science, Los Angeles City Schools, Los Angeles, California.

Pella, Milton O., Professor, The School of Education, University of Wisconsin, Madison.

Reiner, William B., Research Associate, Board of Education of the City of New York, Brooklyn, New York.

Vordenberg, Kenneth E., Supervisor of Science, Secondary Schools, Cincinnati, Ohio.

Washton, Nathan S., Professor of Education, Queens College, Flushing, New York.

APPENDIX IV

BIBLIOGRAPHY

Barbe, Walter B. "Evaluation of Special Classes for the Gifted." *Exceptional Children* 22: 60-62; November 1955.

Barnes, Cyrus D., and others. "Criteria for Selecting Supplementary Reading Science Books for Intellectually Gifted High School Students." *Science Education* 40: 215-18; April 1958.

Baxter, John F., and Bingham, N. Eldred. *Introductory Course in Chemistry*. Wilmette, Illinois: Encyclopaedia Britannica Films, 1959.

Bloom, Samuel W. "The Search for Science Talent." *Science Education* 38: 232-36; April 1954.

Brandwein, Paul F. *The Gifted Student as Future Scientist*. New York: Harcourt, Brace and Company, 1955.

Brown, H. Emmett. *The Development of a Course in the Physical Sciences for the Senior High School of the Lincoln School*. New York: Bureau of Publications, Teachers College, Columbia University, 1939.

Brown, Kenneth E., and Johnson, Philip G. *Education for the Talented in Mathematics and Science*. U. S. Department of Health, Education, and Welfare, Office of Education, Bulletin 1952, No. 15. Washington, D. C.: Superintendent of Documents, Government Printing Office, 1953.

Charney, Sol. *A Teacher's Handbook of Biological Demonstrations for Advanced Science Course in the General Education Programs of Westchester County Secondary Schools*. Unpublished doctor's thesis. New York: Teachers College, Columbia University, 1957.

Cole, Charles C. *Encouraging Scientific Talent.* New York: College Entrance Examination Board, 1956.

Commission on Advanced Placement, Norton, Bayes M., chairman. *Advanced Placement Program.* New York: College Entrance Examination Board, 1956.

Committee on Exceptional Children. *How to Educate the Gifted Child.* New York: Metropolitan School Study Council, 1956.

Committee on Science Education in American Schools of the National Society for the Study of Education. *Science Education in American Schools.* Forty-Sixth Yearbook. Part I. Chicago: University of Chicago Press, 1947.

Donaldson, Robert R. *A Study of Methods for Teaching Rapid Learners in Secondary School Science.* Unpublished doctor's thesis. Ithaca, N. Y.: Cornell University, 1955.

Goldberg, Miriam L. *A Report on Recent Research in the Fields of the Academically Talented.* Reproduced by the National Education Association Project on the Academically Talented Student, October 1958. (Mimeo.)

Goldstein, Philip. *How To Do An Experiment.* New York: Harcourt, Brace and Company, 1957.

Gordon, Garford C. *Providing for Outstanding Science and Mathematics Students.* Southern California Education Monograph, No. 16. Los Angeles: University of Southern California Press, 1955.

Invitational Conference on the Academically Talented Secondary School Pupil. *The Identification and Education of the Academically Talented Student in the American Secondary School.* Washington, D. C.: National Education Association, 1958.

Manufacturing Chemists Association. *Scientific Experiments in Chemistry.* Washington, D. C.: the Association, 1958. (Guide sheets for 31 experiments requiring students to devise their own procedures and to draw original conclusions. Each of the experiments and accompanying guide sheet has been written by an experienced teacher and pilot-tested.)

Meister, Morris. "The Ford Foundation Experiments—Their Implications for the Science Education of High Ability Youth." *Science Teacher* 20: 107-10; April 1953.

Moe, Henry A. "Report of the Committee on Discovery and Development of Scientific Talent." *Science the Endless Frontier, A Report to the President.* (Edited by Vannevar Bush.) Washington, D. C.: Superintendent of Documents, Government Printing Office, 1945. Appendix 4.

National Science Teachers Association. *Action for Students Under the National Defense Education Act*. Washington, D. C.: the Association, a Department of the National Education Association, 1959.

National Science Teachers Association. *Encouraging Future Scientists: Student Projects*. Washington, D. C.: the Association, a Department of the National Education Association, 1958.

National Science Teachers Association. *If You Want To Do a Science Project*. Washington, D. C.: the Association, a Department of the National Education Association, 1955.

National Science Teachers Association. *School Facilities for Science Instruction*. Washington, D. C.: the Association, a Department of the National Education Association, 1954.

National Science Teachers Association. *Standards for Materials and Equipment for the Improvement of Instruction*. Washington, D. C.: the Association, a Department of the National Education Association, 1959.

National Science Teachers Association. *Student Projects*. Revised edition. Washington, D. C.: the Association, a Department of the National Education Association, 1958.

National Society for the Study of Education. *Education of Gifted Children*. Fifty-Seventh Yearbook. Part II. Chicago: University of Chicago Press, 1958.

National Society for the Study of Education. *Special Education for the Gifted Child*. Forty-Ninth Yearbook. Part II. Chicago: University of Chicago Press, 1950.

Newland, T. Ernest. "Essential Research Directions on the Gifted." *Exceptional Children* 21: 291-96; May 1955.

Paulson, Richard, and others. *Laboratory and Field Studies in Biology: A Sourcebook for Secondary Schools*. (Produced by a high-school and college biology teachers conference under a grant from the National Science Foundation. A preliminary draft of the report has been distributed, and the report will be published in early 1960.)

"Physical Science Study: Building a New Structure." *The Science Teacher* 24: 315-30; November 1957. (This series of four articles reports on initiation and progress of the to-date uncompleted Physical Science Study at Massachusetts Institute of Technology, including the preparation of a four-volume textbook, of seventy 20-minute films, and of appropriate teaching materials for the course.)

Physical Science Study Committee. *Physics*. Vols. I and II. Preliminary edition. Cambridge: Massachusetts Institute of Technology, 1957. (First of four volumes of textbooks for a new type of high-school course aimed at presenting pure rather than applied physics. See "Physical Science Study," Section V. The Committee's new address is Watertown, N. Y.)

Physical Science Study Committee, Massachusetts Institute of Technology. *Physical Science Films*. Wilmette, Illinois: Encyclopaedia Britannica Films. (A filmed high-school physics course. See "Physical Science Study," Section V.)

Portland Public Schools. *Science Classes for Exceptionally Endowed Students in the High Schools of Portland, Oregon*. Portland, Oreg.: the Schools, 1957. (Mimeo.)

Raskin, Abraham. *STAR '58*. Washington, D. C.: National Science Teachers Association, a Department of the National Education Association, 1958.

Raskin, Abraham. *STAR 58 Abstracts*. Washington, D. C.: National Science Teachers Association, a Department of the National Education Association, 1959.

Richardson, John S. *School Facilities for Science Instruction*. Washington, D. C.: National Science Teachers Association, a Department of the National Education Association, 1954.

Schenberg, Samuel. *A Study of the Science and Mathematics Courses Elected by the 1956 Senior Class and the Number of Seniors Who Planned to Specialize in Scientific Fields in the Academic High Schools in New York City*. New York: Board of Education of the City of New York, 1957.

Science Service. *Thousands of Science Projects*. Washington, D. C.: the Service, 1953.

U. S. Department of Health, Education, and Welfare, Office of Education. *Teaching Rapid and Slow Learners in High Schools*. Bulletin 1954, No. 5. Washington, D. C.: Superintendent of Documents, Government Printing Office, 1954.

Wald, George. "The Significance of Vertebrate Metamorphosis." *Science*. 128: 1481; December 1958.

White, Harvey E. *Introductory Physics*. Wilmette, Illinois: Encyclopaedia Britannica Films, 1958. A filmed high-school physics course. 162 films in series.

Witty, Paul. *The Gifted Child*. Boston: D. C. Heath and Company, 1951. Chapter 10.

Witty, Paul, and Bloom, Samuel W. "Conserving Ability in the Sciences." *Exceptional Children* 22: 10-16; October 1955.

ACADEMICALLY TALENTED STUDENT PROJECT

Charles E. Bish, Director

NATIONAL EDUCATION ASSOCIATION

Ruth A. Stout, President
William G. Carr, Executive Secretary

Lyle W. Ashby, Deputy Executive Secretary